SCHOOL

Written by Gay Su Pinnell
Illustrated by Peggy Tagel

Scholastic Inc.
New York Toronto London Auckland Sydney
Mexico City New Delhi Hong Kong

ISBN 0-439-13185-5

13 5/0
Printed in China 62

I see crayons.

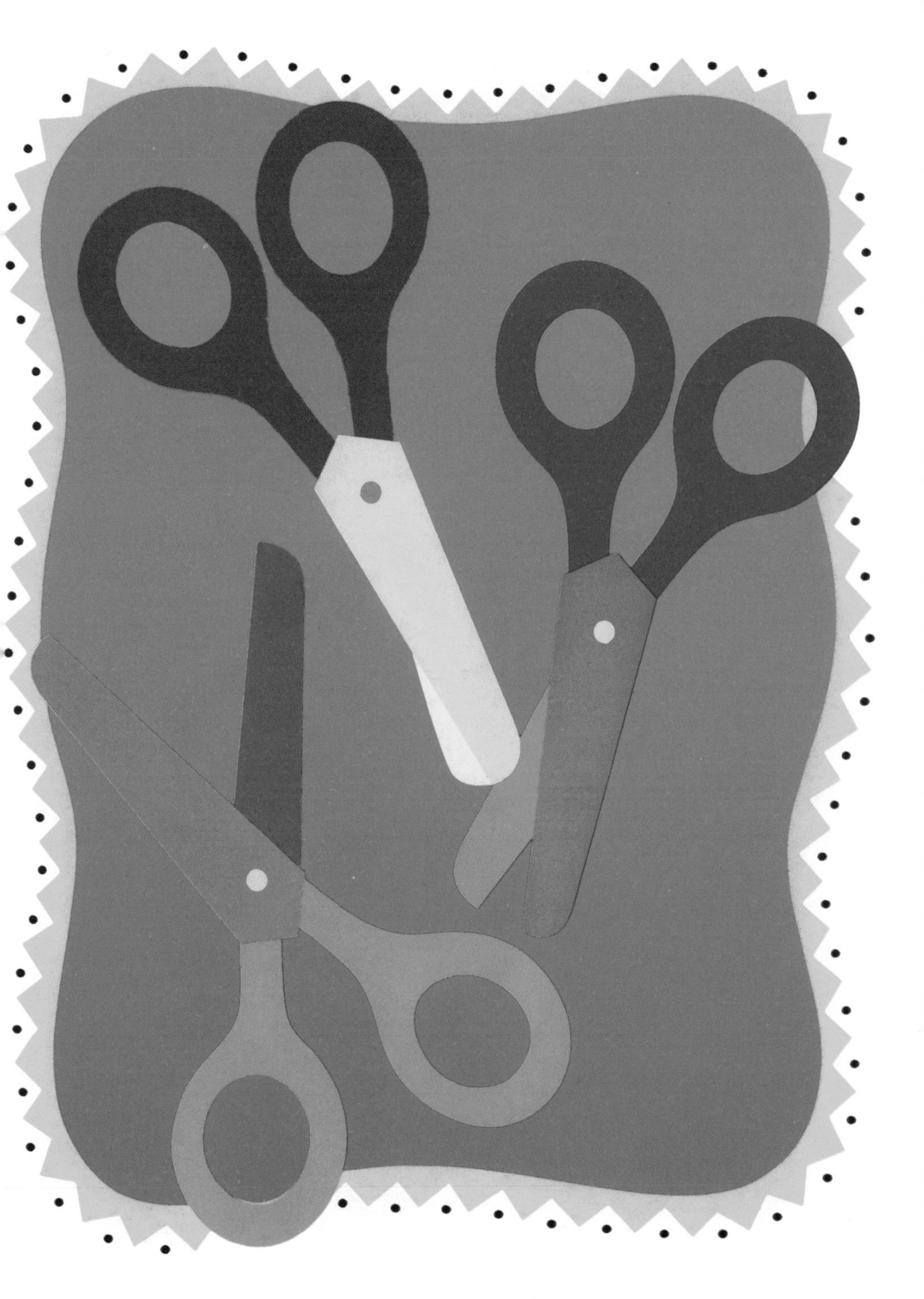

I see scissors.

I see books.

I see desks.

I see chairs.

I see children.

I see school.